A

CHARMED

LIFE

A Charmed Life

by

Little Silver Charm

as told to Diane White

Old Friends Press
Georgetown, Kentucky

A CHARMED LIFE
Copyright © 2016 by Old Friends Press
All Rights Reserved

ISBN 978-0-692-68702-4
LCCN 2016905703

The profits from this book help to support the retired horses at Old Friends Equine.
oldfriendsequine.org

Cover photo by Laura Battles

Design by Frogtown Bookmaker
frogtownbookmaker.com

Old Friends Press
1841 Paynes Depot Rd.
Georgetown, Kentucky 40324

Introduction

I am an extremely modest little horse and yet I'm not surprised when visitors to Old Friends make a point of seeking me out before they ask to meet (Big) Silver Charm, War Emblem, Game On Dude, Sarava, Touch Gold or any of our many retired Thoroughbred champions. I am pretty cute after all. But I'm more than just a pretty face. As I leafed through the pages of *A Charmed Life*, a brilliant collection of photographs of me, many taken by world-class equine photographers, I gained some insight into the secret of my phenomenal appeal. It's not just that I'm adorable, or that I'm incredibly photogenic. I think people respond to my keen intelligence and my independent spirit, qualities that emerge in so many of these photographs and the accompanying remarks from my internationally acclaimed Facebook page. These same qualities moved Michael Blowen, our founder and president, to name me Old Friends' official spokeshorse. I hope you enjoy the photos and my comments and that you will visit me at the farm and on my Facebook page, Little Silver Charm at Old Friends.

Little Silver Charm

Acknowledgments

I would like to thank Lorita M. Lindemann, who found me in a very bad place and helped me escape, and Michael Blowen, who gave me a home and a job.

Beth Shannon, the Frogtown Bookmaker and a tireless Old Friends volunteer, deployed her many talents—writer, artist, graphic designer, horse listener—to produce this book. Thank you, Beth.

And I suppose I have to thank Diane White, although all she did was take dictation from Yours Truly. Thanks Diane, but aren't ghostwriters supposed to remain anonymous?

And my special thanks to photographers...

Laura Battles

John Bradley

Connie Bush

Rick Capone

Kate Dunn

Equisport Photos

Barbara Fossum

Barbara D. Livingston

Vivian Montoya

Joyce Patci

Beth Shannon

Tim Wilson

Diane White

...for so ably capturing the essence of being equine. They also took excellent photos of the big horses.

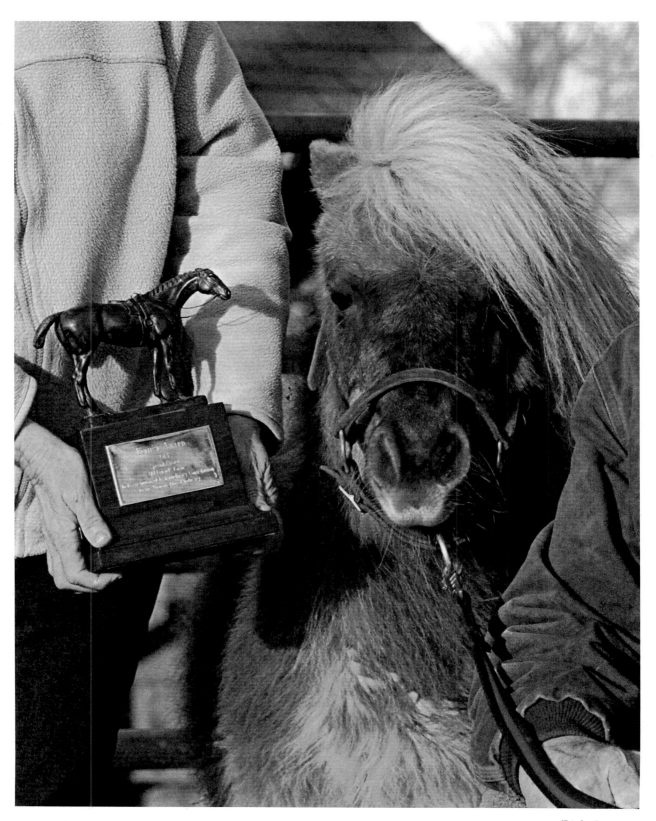

Rick Capone

Old Friends
Thoroughbred
(and one miniature
horse)
Retirement in
Georgetown,
Kentucky

Old Friends Equine, a 501(c)(3) nonprofit, provides a comfortable, dignified retirement home to Thoroughbreds whose racing and breeding days are done.

Old Friends offers tours daily by reservation. To schedule a visit, phone 502-863-1775.

To learn more about our organization and residents, visit us at oldfriendsequine.org

September 7, 2010
I see someone posted that photo of Kent Desormeaux trying, and failing, to ride me. I guess I showed him a thing or two. I may be little, but I won't be trifled with.

Equisport Photos

Equisport Photos

September 12, 2010
Special Ring finally took my advice and learned a trick that he uses to persuade visitors to give him treats. If you say, "Show me your tattoo," he lifts his upper lip to show off his Jockey Club I.D. number. I think some of these Thoroughbreds think they're too good to do tricks, but as I keep telling them, cuteness counts when it comes to getting carrots. I should know.

September 23, 2010

My long ordeal is over. My staff disappeared for a week and I had no one to cater to my needs. Actually, I had any number of people willing to do my bidding but I decided to ignore them and feel sorry for myself. But Michael, my valet, and Diane, my alleged biographer, are back now and I have been trying to make them feel as guilty as possible about abandoning me. More carrots please, and hurry up about it.

My friend Madeleine Grace likes to groom me.

October 10-17 2010

Four hooves up for "Secretariat," my favorite movie ever. And that's not just because the great horse is one of my idols and role models, or that Mrs. Chenery–I call her Penny–is a close personal friend. She didn't hesitate to help a little horse in need–me, actually–when the forces of evil wanted me evicted from my home.

When I first came to Kentucky I lived in Michael's and Diane's backyard in Midway. A nasty man who shall remain nameless–not even a close neighbor–objected, saying that if he couldn't keep chickens in his back yard Michael and Diane shouldn't be able to keep me as a pet. He even went so far as to call me a "farm animal"!

Penny Chenery, Michael and me. I'm the one in the middle.

Penny Chenery graciously lent her support to the "Keep Silver Charm Home" campaign. Michael and Diane collected hundreds of signatures on a petition, and put up posters all over Midway. There was a hearing, an investigation and finally, after a long time, the town attorney issued an opinion ruling that I am officially a pet, not livestock. You can read the full story in my autobiography, if my ghostwriter ever finishes it.

Laura Battles

Barbara D. Livingston

November 16, 2010
Personally, I think height is an overrated quality. A small difference in size, just a few feet or so, should be no barrier to true love. Does anybody know where I might find some elevator horse shoes?

Barbara D. Livingston

December 7, 2010

Dear Santa,

I need your help to meet the Girl of My Dreams, Zenyatta. If I disguised myself as one of your reindeer do you think you could drop me off in her stable when you deliver all her other Christmas gifts?

As ever,

Little Silver Charm

December 23, 2010

A carrot tree!

Just what I've always wanted...

Rick Capone

January 11, 2011
A snowy day at the farm. Snow is my element. I never get cold. I have a coat as thick as a musk ox. And thinking about my Dream Girl keeps me warm. Valentine's Day approaches.

My Dearest Zenyatta,
I'll gallop your way to give you my heart.
Once you meet me, we'll never part.
I'm dashing and handsome & so full of charm.
Be my secret valentine behind the barn.
                    Love,
                    Little Silver Charm
                    XOXOXO

February 14, 2011
Happy Valentine's Day from your biggest fan at Old Friends!

February 25, 2011
I know I'm handsome and irresistible, although it's always nice to hear my own impressions confirmed by others. Maybe it is just winter weight.

Laura Battles

Laura Battles

Maybe–to borrow a line from Garfield–I'm not fat, just fluffy.

6

Equisport Photos

March 26, 2011
My good friend The Wicked North passed away on Thursday. I miss him very much. As you know, one of my many jobs here at Old Friends is helping new arrivals adjust to retirement, which is easier said than done, in some cases, if you get my drift. But Wicked never needed my help. He was at home here from the moment he set hoof on the farm

The Wicked North and I had a lot in common. He was handsome, affable, highly intelligent and charming. And so am I. He took to retirement gracefully, and I should know, I wrote the book on equine retirement, "Little Silver Charm's Big Book of Horse Retirement." *Ave atque Vale*, old friend. To know you was to love you.

July 1, 2011
I can't believe she cuts up fresh strawberries for that international has-been Creator.

August 17, 2011
Someone has to keep these stallions in line and I'm the only one who can do the job.

August 26, 2011
I've been so busy this week. My dear friend Angie - Miss Dickinson to you - came to Old Friends this week to visit me. She also looked in on Afternoon Deelites, who used to be associated with her ex, Burt Bacharach. But mainly she came here to spend some quality time with yours truly.

August 28, 2011
Angie thinks I need to use more conditioner on my mane. She also suggested that I tease it a little on top, for added height.

September 1, 2011
The memorial for Noor was a fitting tribute to an exceptional champion, a stallion who reminds me a wee bit of myself in that he was adored by all who knew him. Some of the visitors brought carrots, too, and I ate them in Noor's honor.

September 4, 2011
Do you think this "honoring by food" thing could catch on? Today I think I will remember the late Taylor's Special by eating as many carrots as possible in his honor. Taylor was a good friend who taught me a lot. I miss him.

Kate Dunn

September 7, 2011
All the horses are very happy about the change in weather. They've all been running around like crazy. Even Creator has abandoned his usual dignified pose to caper about like a two-year old.

Laura Battles

September 9, 2011

Hidden Lake is ready for her close-up. A reporter from *The Blood-Horse* is coming today to interview her for their series on fabulous retired mares. I may have to add her photo to my pin-up collection. That girl can still run like the wind. And I know because she always runs away from me, unfortunately.

Left & below: Barbara D. Livingston

September 18, 2011

I hear through the Horse Code grapevine that there will be a miniature horse jumping contest next Saturday at the Secretariat Festival.

September 21, 2011
I'm a babe magnet. Everybody says so.

Above & right: Barbara D. Livingston

The camera loves me, but did you know I'm also quite the artist's muse? Here I am in a portrait drawn by Jack Nicholson several years ago. Everyone admires it so much that it's featured on notecards sold in the Old Friends gift shop. Because I'm a very modest little horse I won't mention that the cards are a popular item.

October 15, 2011
I see that my friend Ogygian is the NTRA Aftercare Horse of the Month.

Beth's profile of Big O is great except for one little omission: me. Nowhere does she mention the crucial role I played in teaching Ogygian how to retire. When he first arrived at Old Friends he was stressed from his long trip from Japan. Who taught him to relax and lounge around the paddock?

And who taught him that twirling and rearing trick? And how to act cute so visitors will give him more carrots? Me, me, me! That's who.

October 27, 2011
Last night we welcomed our new stallion, You And I. He came all the way from Washington State in a big fancy truck. There was a beautiful mare on board too, but he didn't offer to introduce me. I have to admit that You and I is a handsome fellow, not as handsome as I am, of course, but very good-looking, for his age.

November 4, 2011
That's Marquetry and me in the photograph, taken not long after he arrived at Old Friends. I was giving him some advice about adjusting to retirement. I'm an expert on retirement, even though I'm not retired myself. In fact, I'm the hardest working horse on the farm.

December 13, 2011

Merry Christmas 2011

Rick Capone

January 2, 2012
Happy New New Year to all my Friends, Old and Young. My New Year's resolution is to trim down, get in shape and make myself even more attractive. My personal trainer, Michael, is helping me with my new exercise program.

March 17, 2012
My old friend Fortunate Prospect has gone the way of all good horses. He was a true gentleman, with a playful streak. He was my role model. I will miss him.

Equisport Photos

May 29, 2012

Michael tells me that some horse named Rapid Redux will be arriving here tomorrow morning. Michael says he won 22 races in a row, more consecutive wins than even the Love of My Life, Zenyatta, racked up. Michael says he's a star. Big deal, I say. Can he play soccer? Does he have a beautiful silver mane and tail? Is he adorable? We'll see.

Laura Battles

June 22, 2012

The famous equine photographer Barbara Livingston visited Old Friends this week to take photos of me.

Barbara D. Livingston

She photographed some of the other horses too, but I think that mainly she was interested in yours truly, and who could blame her?

Don't hate me because I'm beautiful

The wild stallion in me emerges..

Photos by Barbara D Livingston

She got some good photos of me racing Prized.

October 19, 2012
My friend Shari Voltz sent me cookies!

October 23, 2012
Rosie Napravnik! My favorite jockey. And she didn't even try to sit on me! I think I'm in love. Again. – with Rosie Napravnik at Old Friends.

Grazing with friends on a beautiful day. What more could a little horse ask for? Except maybe a few carrots. – at Old Friends.

December 24, 2012

I love Christmas. It's a time of giving and sharing. I like the giving part, especially when I'm on the receiving end.

> A poem (sort of), for the holiday:
> A rainbow of lights on my own little tree,
> Piles of carrots, all for me,
> Gingersnaps and peppermints and gingerbread men
> I can keep for myself
> Or share, if I must.
> It's Christmas. I give all my friends
> The gift of myself.

Barbara D. Livingston

February 2, 2013

My friend Marquetry is gone and I am very, very sad. Some of the stallions here don't know what to make of me, because even though I'm a stallion too, I am so much smaller than they are. They make snarky remarks. Some are even hostile. Marquetry accepted me for what I am and never looked down on me, except in the literal sense. He had a big heart and a generous spirit. His stall overlooks my paddock. He always shared his evening carrots with me. He could have demanded them all, but he made sure there were some for me, too. So many people loved him. I loved him too.

Marquetry

Barbara D. Livingston

February 7, 2013
Please be my valentine.

Her hair is red, her eyes are green,
She's the loveliest jockey I've ever seen.
Rosie Napravnik came to visit one day.
We ran and we played then she went away.
Rosie, O Rosie
I worship you from afar.
That's how it must be, because you're a big star.
And I'm just a little horse
Who sends you his love
On Valentine's Day.

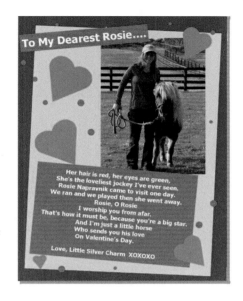

February 18, 2013
Joseph Bokan and his dad Joe came all the way from Saratoga Springs, New York just to see me. Here's Joseph and me in the living room watching HRTV with Michael. I was giving them some handicapping tips.

April 25, 2013
I've had so many visitors lately. A very friendly group of students from Shanghai said that I was their favorite Old Friends horse. No surprise there, right? They wrote out my name in Chinese and told me it's pronounced yin se mei nan.

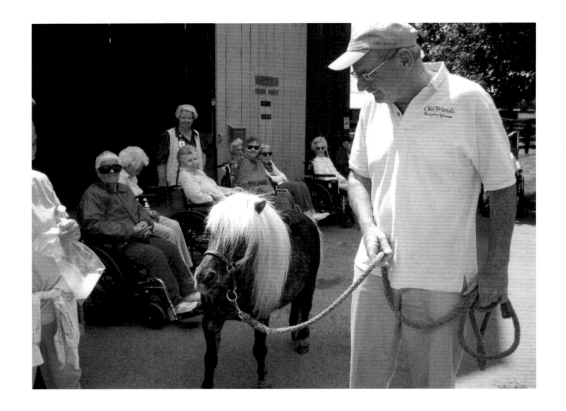

August 15, 2013
Greetings fellow Carrotheads! I entertained some friends from the Sayre Christian Village yesterday. I was at my most charming and they had a ball, if I do say so myself. Michael helped, telling stories about the other horses at Old Friends, but it was pretty plain that they were more interested in getting to know yours truly.

Though I must admit that big horses can be cute too.
Fergus Mac Roich and He Loves Me Not.

September 18, 2013
Jonah Carmine and Carla Angeli learn the finer points of modeling from supermodel Little Silver Charm. Carla learns how to display the merchandise at the Little Silver Charm School of modeling. Cute outfit. – with Carla Angeli Gonzalez Modeling.

The kids have already launched their modeling careers, but they felt some fine tuning by a highly-regarded professional model like me could only help.

When it comes to being adorable, I wrote the book. Obviously Carla has studied my technique.

Jonah has a lot to learn about proper foot placement in photographs. I strike my stallion pose, and ask him to do the same, but he'd rather fool around. Kids.

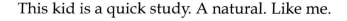

How to wear the hat. Note the all-important jaunty angle.

This kid is a quick study. A natural. Like me.

October 4, 2013
Me and my favorite jockey. I taught her everything she knows about modeling.

Starting November 1st!

Fifth Annual

"Hats Off to the Horses"
Derby Hat Auction to Benefit
OLD FRIENDS of KY

Sponsored by
MAGGIE MAE DESIGNS®

Thank you
Rosie Napravnik & Charmie
for helping us
spread the word!!

Photo - www.equisportphotos.com

Equisport photos. To see more fabulous hats, visit maggiemae.com

Wow. I think Rosie and I were meant for each other.

This wind is doing wonders for my hair.

I am thinking of changing my name to Mini Mucho Macho Man

Sunshine Forever. Equisport Photos

January 8, 2014
The Old Friends family wants to thank everyone for the support and kind words. Patton and Sunshine will be sorely missed but never forgotten.

Patton. Laura Battles

February 11, 2014
Today Clever Allemont is 32 years old. Happy Birthday, Clever! Extra carrots all around! The cards and donations have been coming in all week. Our good friend Dr. Val Nicholson brought Clever a beautiful carrot cake from Granny's Goodies in Georgetown. It was mainly for the humans, but Michael let me have a very small piece. It was delicious, especially the icing.

Laura Battles

March 27, 2014. Me and my new friend London. Aren't we adorable?

photos by Barbara D. Livingston

Here are Michael and I showing Catlaunch and Old Friends' farm manager Tim Wilson how to pose for a conformation photo. Catlaunch is one of the tallest horses at Old Friends. I'm sure that if I had been born a Thoroughbred I would have been a multiple stakes winner like he is.

And here I am with Rosie Napravnik up. We would probably have won the Triple Crown.

Photo tweeted by @RosieNapravnik 27 June 2014

But Fate intervened, and here I am, a little on the short side but nevertheless the idol of thousands of besotted fans.

March 11, 2014
I'm going to miss The Name's Jimmy. I got to know him when he was staying in the big barn, in the stall overlooking my little paddock. We shared a passionate interest in carrots. I was always happy to share my evening snack with him and I know he appreciated my generosity. He often told me so. I enjoyed his stories about his triumphs on the track, but the story I liked best was the one about how he got caught up in Hurricane Katrina and got lost in the Louisiana swamp for two days and could have been eaten by alligators, but thanks to his speed and intelligence and quick reflexes, wasn't. He led an exciting life and I am happy to have been a small, a very small, part of it. Hail and farewell, old friend.

Old Friends' 2014 Easter Egg Race Meet

Sunday evening's race card featured Little Silver Charm's challenge to all comers. The gutsy little contender strutted onto the green April turf, ready to try a match race with any who dared. No horse is too famous, no graded stakes winner too fleet, for the diminutive, but dauntless, LSC to take on.

Before post time the spectators' scene seethed with activity.

Michael phoned in his final bets.

Beth got some hot tips from Ogygian.

Bebe, occupying the best box, seemed more interested in just being seen.

For the first race on the card, Little Silver Charm paraded to the top of the run, with Michael Blowen up. Or rather, beside. There his opponent awaited him– None other than the always-game Swan's Way. Swannie, a 25 year old bay with the formidable experience of 81 starts under his belt, was on his toes, ready for any challenge.

…And they're off!

Little Silver Charm broke sharply. Seizing the lead, he dashed down the track, mane and tail flying in the sunset.

…until Swannie had no choice but to charge into a full trot.

Swan's Way's longer strides swallowed the ground and he passed the mighty mini for a three length win

Johannesbourbon enjoys the action.

Johannesbourbon, Diane, John, Kiri's Clown, Laura, Beth and Prized cheered them on from their spots right on the rail.

But Little Silver Charm wasn't ready to throw in the towel. Not yet. Maybe a jump up in class was what he really needed.

What about the 1989 Breeders' Cup Turf winner, Prized? Would the grand old campaigner dare to try the Miniscule Monster at his own game?

Little Silver Charm decided a jockey change might help. So he fired Michael and welcomed John Bradley aboard. Now the star of the farm, the Chaser of Dreams was rarin' to go again!

But Prized pulled a strategic surprise...

...He turned and ran in the other direction.

Just as all seemed over, Prized revved up his famous closing style. Steadily the Breeders' Cup Turf winner diminished the distance at a decidedly swift walk. At the very least, he was curious to see what the mini was up to.

But it was too late. Little Silver Charm passed the last fence post well ahead. Prized decided he was more interested in nibbling some more grass, anyway.

Little Silver Charm and his connections celebrate with ginger snaps in the winner's circle.

Little Silver Charm and Michael head back to the barn after a successful race day.

A Grade One Easter was had by all.

Easter Egg Meet coverage by Beth Shannon
Photos by Laura Battles

June 3, 2014

Everyone wants to know my pick for the Belmont but how can I concentrate on my handicapping with goats in my paddock. Goats! Two of them. They arrived yesterday with Eldaafer, who won the Breeder's Cup Marathon a few years ago. Apparently the goats go everywhere with him.

And now they are here. The neighborhood has gone to hell.

As you may have noticed, Eldaafer and his goats, whose names are Google and Yahoo, are in my paddock. I certainly notice it.

When a new horse comes to live at Old Friends, they go through a brief quarantine period. During this period, they split their time between a stall and turn-out in a special quarantine area near the barn. There they are observed, get checkups from the vet, and get used to their new home. I agree that routine quarantine of new residents is a wise precaution.

Sometimes, too, a horse needs to rest in a stall part of the time, but gets turn-out time for fresh air and exercise each day in a controlled space near the barn. Wallenda tells me he likes this routine.

What I do not see is why it's my paddock that has been appropriated for these purposes. Along with my run-in shed. And my pinup of Zenyatta.

Who's that in my paddock?

Johannesbourbon.
In my paddock.

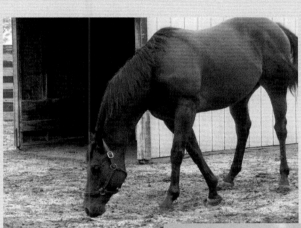

Amazombie.
In
my
paddock.

Geronimo.
In my paddock.

Wallenda.
In my paddock.

Eldaafer stepped on my soccer ball.

Call Roger Goodell.

MY paddock with MY name on it.

June 23, 2014

They're building me a new paddock at the top of the hill so that I can greet every visitor personally. At least that's what they tell me. All I know is that there are a lot building materials piled up behind the gazebo, but nothing's happening. The management tells me that I'll be getting my own goat-free run-in shed, too. I asked for a Jacuzzi, but I haven't seen any sign of it yet.

I have ordered a "Goat-Free Zone" sign for my new paddock.

September 6, 2014
My ghost writer calls this the photo op of the year. Hmmm. Perhaps. I prefer to call it the continuation of a beautiful friendship. I admit, Creator and I were a little taken aback to BOTH be in the barn at the same time. I personally like to think of us both as rugged outdoorsmen....with a custom run-in shed, daily room service and lots of treats, of course!

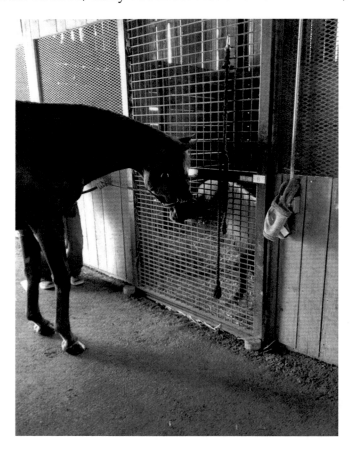

September 26, 2014
It's finished! My new paddock at last! And the best part? No goats allowed!

October 8, 2014
Game on Dude and Amazombie arrived yesterday. You wouldn't believe all the fuss. Naturally all the media people wanted to know what I think of our new arrivals. I was pleasantly surprised by how professionally they conducted themselves, in contrast to some of our other, less refined retirees who stormed off the truck like hooligans and proceeded to behave as if they were born in a barn.

Game on Dude and Yankee Fourtune admire me.

November 5, 2014
Our friend Sam Gooding came out from the Kentucky Horseshoeing School the other day...they brought out a lot of farriers to trim all of the horses' feet, and they even brought one my own size to do mine! Pictured in this photo by Tim Wilson are LSC, Michael and Sam's son, Josh honing his farrier skills

November 30, 2014

My idol, Silver Charm, will be arriving this week and I admit I'm nervous. I have worshipped him from afar these many years, now I will be meeting him in person. What if he doesn't like me? Even worse, what if everybody forgets about ME in their excitement over meeting HIM? I hope some of my friends will show up Tuesday at the open house to let me know that they still adore me.

(Big) Silver Charm Arrives!

December 1, 2014

The anticipation builds.

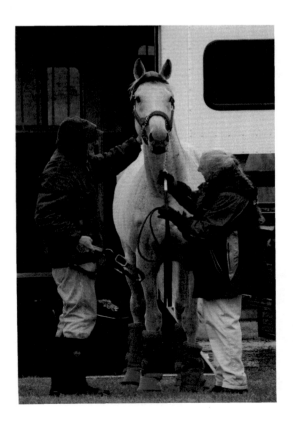

When my famous namesake stepped out of the trailer, who should be with him but his old groom and buddy, Three Chimneys Farm's Stallion Manger, Sandy Hatfield. Because Sandy brought him to Old Friends, Silver Charm immediately decided this is a good place to be.

December 2, 2014
When Silver Charm had enjoyed a night's rest, I held an open house so his many fans could welcome him home. I must admit I'm an excellent host.

Sandy, Silver Charm, and our adoring fans.

Photos by Laura Battles

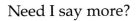

Need I say more?

January 2, 2015
I'm looking forward to the new season of "Downton Abbey." Will Lady Mary ever find a stallion worthy of her? I didn't think much of the suitors who were sniffing around her at the end of the last season. And what about Lady Edith's secret foal? I can't wait!

January 2, 2015
There should be a part for a little horse in "Downton Abbey." Don't those kiddies need a pony? Not just any little horse, of course, but one that would feel as comfortable in the nursery or the library as he would in the stable or on the hunt.

It's a sure fire ratings booster.

I have a rich fantasy life.

January 17, 2015
Guess who is Carolyn Coburn's next favorite horse after California Chrome? That's right! Yours Truly. Here she is with her husband Steve holding one of her prized possessions - a framed photograph of me!

January 23, 2015
Here' are Michael and Diane thanking me for helping Old Friends win an Eclipse Award.

February 6, 2015
One more Valentine for the girl I love.

> Zenyatta, perfect mare
>
> Spare a thought for me
> A little horse
> Who loves you from afar,
> Who knows that it can never be,
> But who adores you.
> On Valentine's Day
> And every other day.
> You are always with me.
> Other loves come and go
> But you are forever,
> Juliet to my Romeo.

February 17, 2015
Our barn manager Tim Wilson captured these photos of yours truly enjoying a snow day after our recent winter storm.

Laura Battles

The Great Profile.
John Barrymore has nothing on me!

Equisport Photos

February 27, 2015
Thought for the Day: Sometimes less is more. On second thought, less is always more, if you're a miniature horse.

Equisport Photos

March 1, 2015
I am devastated by the loss of my good friend Creator. We had a special bond.

Laura Battles

Joyce Patci

46

Laura Battles

Laura Battles

March 19, 2015
This is how I will remember my friend Ogygian. He was magnificent.

Beth Shannon

March 19, 2015
And so...this happened today. Have no idea why ANYONE would think that Google goat is cute, and-or entertaining. Ah well, doesn't take much to please some folks...two or four footed...ahem, talkin' to you El D.

You put your right hoof in, you put your left goat out.

"Let's boogie!"
  says Google.

"Dancing" my foot. It looks to me like Google is in attack mode.

Jasmine, Eldaafer & Google. Photos by Tim Wilson.

48

March 23, 2015
Getting to know my idol, Silver Charm.

The pear tree was donated by Old Friends friend Tim Ford in honor of Creator. Everybody knows Creator loved strawberries, but pears were his favorite fruit, as long as they were high quality and perfectly *al dente*. One Christmas a secret admirer sent him a box of Harry & David Royal Riviera pears. He loved them. So did I. He shared one with me. After he died, the people at Harry & David tweeted their condolences, saying that obviously he had good taste. Indeed he did.

In this photo I'm working on my jumping skills, getting ready for the summer's tours.

April 9, 2015
While Gary Stevens was visiting the OTHER Silver Charm, I made friends with his daughter, Maddie.

She kept saying, "He's just my size."

I think I see a mini in her near future.

April 19, 2015
We had a special guest this week. The great Angel Cordero. As he has won, among many other things, three Kentucky Derbies, and I am the senior advisor here at Old Friends, we had much to discuss regarding this year's Run for the Roses. Angel was also aboard my friend, Gulch during his Breeders Cup Sprint victory. Thanks to Tim Wilson for these photos.

April 20, 2015

My dance card is so full this month, my little hooves are tired! But it's always a pleasure, as the official spokeshorse for Old Friends, to welcome new and returning visitors!

Photos by Barbara D. Livingston

This morning, we had a surprise visit this morning from Steve and Caroline Coburn, co-owners of Derby and Preakness winner California Chrome. They dropped by to say hello and visit with their favorite Old Friends horse, why yours truly, of course!

May 20, 2015
Happy Birthday Mixed Pleasure!

June 23, 2015

Can I eat it? Or should I try to make friends with it? Well, at least it's not a goat.

We have Snappers in the pond. I stay away from them. This is a friendly turtle. I think.

June 30, 2015 ·
Thought for the Day:

When life
gives you lemons
ask for carrots instead.

July 5, 2015
Rosie brought her baby, Carson, to the farm to meet me.

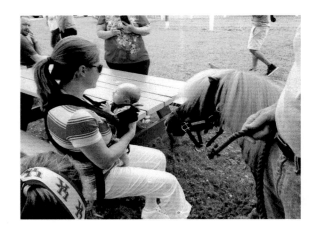 

July 6, 2015
I'm very proud and happy to be Carson's very first horse. I hope he'll remember me when he's a champion jockey like his beautiful mom. I love you Rosie!

July 17, 2015
Me and The Man, Joe Torre

Mr. John took this photo.

54

By the way, Mr. John, of John Bradley Designs in Horse Hair, has been keeping me looking handsome for all my friends and admirers.

Barbara D. Livingston

My personal stylist John Bradley and I are giving Silver Charm some grooming tips. I'm not sure he appreciated our advice.

Barbara D. Livingston

July 19, 2015
Boy Scout Troop 400, affiliated with the Elkhorn Baptist Church, created a handsome base for our "dancing horses" statue, donated by artist and Old Friends supporter Fred Krakowiak. The base was Justin DeRosa's Eagle Scout project. I was happy to give it the highly coveted Little Silver Charm stamp of approval. Four enthusiastic hooves up!

And now Princess has a new favorite spot...

July 21, 2015
Hello ladies.

August 8, 2015
My good friend Karen Bailey of the Kentucky Wildlife Center was bitten by a fox she was trying to help. Karen, if I've told you once I've told you a hundred times: Don't go sticking your fingers in foxes' mouths! Personally, I would never bite your hand, especially if you were feeding me carrots. All my love to a beautiful lady.

August 17, 2015
I learned this trick from Special Ring.
Now can I have a carrot?

September 29, 2015
Thank you to Laura Battles for capturing this photo....I like to call it...Little Silver Charm at Liberty.

And this one by Matt and Wendy Woolley I call Wisdom

Equisport Photos

September 29, 2015

Here I am helping Michael with final edits for Dan Rhema's upcoming book, *Little Silver Charm*, obviously a story all about me, even though Dan Rhema has hogged all the credit for writing it. Little did I imagine when I engaged him to work with me on the book that he would seize control of the project and try to claim that he was the only author.

October 22, 2015

Take it from Yours Truly, this is a fabulous book, a riveting tale of intrigue, mistaken identity, amnesia and passion. Well, maybe not passion, it is a story for children, although adults will enjoy it too.

November 9, 2015
Pride and Prejudice on TCM! One of my favorite movies. I'd love to play Mr Darcy opposite Zenyatta. "In vain have I struggled. It will not do...you must allow me to say how ardently I admire and love you."

Planning my holiday image

Psst, Mr. John,
    absolutely no girlie braids.ribbons or bows.
       I am a stallion, after all.

Vivian Montoya

Thank you for making me look so handsome.
Now I'm going to roll in the mud.

December 24, 2015
Merry Christmas to all my friends out there in Charmie's World. I plan to celebrate the holday by distributing carrots and treats to everyone on the farm. Even the goats.

The many faces of me.

Photos by Rick Capone

Addressing the Ball

Barbara D. Livingston

The perfect shot! I'm a soccer star--just ask me.

A post-soccer kiss, to show we're friends even though I'm a much better player than Michael.

About the Author

LITTLE SILVER CHARM's origins are shrouded in mystery. His journey to super-stardom began in 2001 at Rockingham Park race track in New Hampshire, when he was rescued by Lorita Lindemann from a truck headed to the slaughter auction. Michael named him Little Silver Charm after his all-time favorite horse. When Michael and his wife Diane moved to Midway, Kentucky, Little Silver Charm's talent for public relations became obvious to everyone who met him. When Michael started Old Friends he naturally named Little Silver Charm the organization's official spokeshorse and mascot. He began his Facebook blog in August 2010. The rest is history. Now Charmie, as he's known to his intimate friends, presides over Old Friends' herd of more than 150 Thoroughbreds, including many famous champions, among them Kentucky Derby winners Silver Charm and War Emblem, and Belmont Stakes winners Touch Gold and Sarava.

Also about me from Old Friends Press:

LITTLE SILVER CHARM
by
Dan Rhema

Little Silver Charm, a miniature horse with a bump on his head and no memory, finds himself the newest resident at Old Friends Farm, a home for retired Thoroughbred racehorses.

Little Silver Charm is an imaginative, engaging book, filled with charming characters–old friends and some new ones, too–along with an incorrigible villain to add spice to the mix. Goodness and love triumph in the end, of course, as they forever should.

Bill Mooney, Eclipse Award-winning turf writer

Dan Rhema captures the spirit of Old Friends and its resident good-luck charm, Little Silver Charm, in this enjoyable novel that will introduce young readers to the great work being done at this wonderful equine retirement facility.

Jay Privman, award-winning writer with *Daily Racing Form* and proud Old Friends supporter

Available at the Old Friends gift shop,
at oldfriendsequine.org
and
on Amazon.com

50% of this book's profits help support the equine residents of Old Friends.

Made in the USA
Middletown, DE
02 October 2016